I Can Do This

I Can Do This

living with cancer
tracing a year of hope

Beverlye Hyman Fead

Santa Barbara Cancer Center
Wellness Program Publishing

Santa Barbara Cancer Center
Wellness Program Publishing
Santa Barbara, CA
© 2004 Beverlye Hyman Fead
All rights reserved. Published 2004
Third Printing 2008
Reproductions of orchids and self
portrait are derived from original
paintings by Beverlye Hyman Fead
Printed in the United States of America
ISBN: 0-9761483-0-7

Cover; "Tears" self portrait by Beverlye Hyman Fead

*To my grandmother, mother,
and two sisters who lost
their lives to cancer.*

*To the men and women
who spend their lives
looking for a cure
for this disease.*

CONTENTS

FOREWORD

What courage and strength it takes to thank your cancer for all the blessings life offers. Beverlye Hyman Fead does just this in her moving memoir that traces her fears, struggles, and joys through a year of treatment.

Her prose and poetry is a generous gift of love and hope to all those who live with cancer and those who love them. *I Can Do This* is a book you want to have by your bedside during long hours of the night.

> PERIE LONGO, PHD
> Poet Laureate of Santa Barbara
> President, National Association
> for Poetry Therapy
> Author of *The Privacy of Wind*

INTRODUCTION

Who hasn't been touched by cancer? Someone you know, a family member, a friend, possibly even yourself. I have cancer like lots of people do. What makes me unusual is that as of this writing, I've beaten the odds by living with cancer, surprising my doctors and myself. I was given two months to live, twenty-four months ago.

People ask me where I got my strength. Some may be born with it, but I think mine was cultivated. The same kind of resolve that helps me stand up to this cancer I remember feeling as a little girl. My parents traveled and left me alone a great deal. I can still feel myself standing straight as they drove away, my hands on my hips saying to myself, *I can do this!*

Some things don't change. Sixty-some years later, after receiving my cancer diagnosis, I am still saying to myself – *I can do this!*

DISCOVERY

Lie down, he says kindly. *Let's feel your stomach.* At first his hands touch my abdomen lightly, tapping here and there. Then he probes deeper. It hurts.

How long has this been going on? He asks.

Quite a long time, I say.

For a while now, I have lived with a grabbing, stabbing kind of pain that comes and goes. Somehow I made adjustments to it. Looking back, I can't imagine how or why I would do that, given my history. The only explanation is denial working overtime.

Let's take an x-ray, Kurt, my dear doctor friend, says.

A few hours later I am back in his office, my x-rays aglow on the panel of lights behind him. There was a mass.

A mass of what? I ask, feeling the first wave of shock hit.

It could be a lot of things, Beverlye. It could be adhesions from your hysterectomy or —

I know the answer but ask anyway. *Or what?*

He takes some time answering. *We need to rule out stomach cancer.*

Anger hits next. *What are you talking about? I'm working out. I've never been in better shape. It's just a sore stomach.* I feel fear climb up my throat. I swallow hard and stare at him. Expecting what, I don't know. Hoping he never said those words but when I look back at him I know he has.

My doctor finally breaks the silence and says in his very quiet voice, *Let's just take some more tests to be sure.*

Blood test (negative), colonoscopy (crowded). *Crowded? What does that mean?* Endoscopy (nothing). *Probably an adhesion.*

One more test, a laparoscopy. As I was coming out of the anesthesia, I could hear my doctor telling my family how serious it was. Terror struck my heart. It would be weeks before the primary source and the final diagnosis would be disclosed.

And so the dance begins.

THE DANCE

And so the dance begins.
The orchestra is playing.
Many a time I've heard this tune.
I've seen these steps before.
My body sways to the music.
Does this song have heartbreak waiting
at the bridge?
Or a happy ending at last?
Only the Maestro knows for sure —
Will He give me a sign?
How will I know?
How long can I keep dancing?

WHERE HAVE YOU BEEN?

You've been in my thoughts;
You've been in my psyche;
You've been in my genes.
Where have you been?
You're late, you know: I've been
looking for you.
You've been in my memory.
You came for a moment years ago.
There are no *Oh no*'s or *Why me?*
How could this be?
There is only – *Where have you been?*
I've been waiting for you!

In the Beginning

The first month or so after my cancer was discovered, I wandered around in a fog looking for a place to put my feelings. I was fortunate to find it.

For years I had worked as a volunteer for the Santa Barbara Cancer Center, raising money as well as designing a new lobby for cancer patients with the help of my architect friend, Don Nulty. I wanted people fighting the disease to have a room that was warm and welcoming, with couches and cushy pillows, a TV, and a play area for children. We called it the Fisher Living Room in honor of the women in my family. Fisher was my maiden name.

I had become very fond of the Cancer Center president Rick Scott and his staff. I called Christine Pickett who runs the Center's Patient Wellness Program. I was so confused, I could barely speak. Later she told me how fragile I sounded. She took care not to overwhelm me with too much information, but did suggest I enroll in one of the many classes the Center offered patients. Nothing sounded good until she mentioned a poetry class.

Maybe I'll try that one, I said.

You'll love it, Beverlye, said Christine. *The facilitator is a gentle person and a wonderful poet.*

I was nervous about my ability to write, but desperate for a place to put my feelings, so I gave it a try. I loved it from the first minute I put pen to paper. The paradox of this class was that we all came to write, but in silence we understood one another.

The Fisher girls

Mother

THE DIAMOND EARRINGS

I was twenty-nine when my mother
distributed her jewelry.
Large pieces, small pieces,
Diamonds, platinum, gold necklaces,
Earrings, bracelets, pins, rings.
I want you to have them while I'm still alive,
She said to her three daughters.
My father bought this jewelry for my mother.
I thought all husbands did this.
I learned they do not.
My mother never cared about jewelry;
She wore it to please my father.
Although my mother was very sick,
She had thought about this very carefully.
Thelma, she whispered, *I want you to have*
the most diamonds.
Your family is in financial turmoil.
Take the diamond watch,
the diamond bracelets, and the big diamond ring.
Beverlye, you're the baby.
Take the diamond earrings, small diamond bracelet,
Diamond heart, and diamond and gold pin.
Eileen – her voice was weaker now –
You and your husband are very successful.
Here is your jewelry, some gold bracelets,
Gold necklaces, gold rings.
It was only a few days later that my mother died.
In my father's arms, with her girls all around her.

Two days went by and I couldn't stand it.
I went to Thelma, the eldest, and said,
We must give Eileen diamonds.
She cares about them more than you and I.
Eileen, we said, *these things got mixed up in our pile.*
And I gave her my diamond earrings,
Thelma gave her a diamond bracelet.
Now we all had Mother's diamonds.
Two weeks later a thief broke into my house
and took all my jewelry and my mementos
of my mother.
Five years later my eldest sister died,
leaving her jewelry to her daughter,
who in times of trouble sold it.
Twenty years later my sister Eileen lay dying
in her bed,
With her three sons and husband
surrounding her.
Eileen and I looked alike,
talked alike, walked alike,
but were very different.
We chose different lives.
She was a businessperson,
dressed to the hilt every day.
I was a rebel,
a painter, a searcher, a jeans-person,
a get-on-the-floor-and-play-with-your-kids person.
We adored and were jealous of each other.
Those last days we spilled out all our love.
We talked about Mother, Dad,

Thelma, all the good things.
She asked her husband
if she could have some time alone with me.
I have something for you, she said when they all left.
She pulled out the earrings from under her pillow.
My long ago dearly missed Mother's
diamond earrings.
We both cried.
Did she ever know they were meant for me?
It didn't matter.

Eileen

Before the Diagnosis

It took time to get the final diagnosis. Those few weeks were by far the worst. At night, I lay awake in disbelief and cried. During the day, I cried some more. Sadness and fear were my constant companions. I was so sad I wouldn't see my grandchildren grow up, so sad for my husband and my kids. I had gone through cancer deaths with my family and knew what was ahead of us. I wanted to be brave for them. I wanted to do this gracefully. Not once during this time did I ever dare to believe I'd pull out of it. Even the constant caring from my friends and family wasn't enough to stop my fears. My husband Bob, my children Terry and Jim, and their respective mates, Eric and Leslie, stayed with me constantly. Even with families of their own they went to every doctor's meeting, did research, talked to the doctors privately, and virtually did not leave my side for the first month. My daughter's soft hand was always in mine. We were like a band of gypsies traveling to each procedure. Tape recorder, bottles of water, snacks for sustenance, and always joking to cover up our anxiety.

To manage my feelings, I did two things. At night as I lay awake unable to sleep, I made lists of all that had to be done. My husband Bob and I had begun a remodeling project in our new house. Every room was ripped apart. What to do now? Either remodel or sell. More lists. We continued remodeling. I also worked on getting my affairs in order. I wanted to make sure Bob and the children received what I wanted them to have. This angered my husband.

One day when I asked him if he wanted this painting or that, he barked back, *Don't talk about it, Bev. I don't care what painting I get or if I get any!*

But I care, I replied and continued making lists and organizing my affairs- I had to. It comforted me and gave me a sense of control.

When we first heard the news, Bob cried often but once the shock wore off, his anger took over. He seemed angry all the time. I didn't understand it. I felt hurt.

Finally, he broke down. *You eat right! You exercise! Goddamn it, Bev! Why did this happen to you?*

I was so relieved he finally was able to express his feelings. So was he. Once that happened, we faced our common enemy, cancer, together.

During this time, Alice Sebold's stunning novel, *The Lovely Bones*, hit the bestseller lists. I was drawn to this story about a girl who was raped and murdered. After her death, she narrates the story from heaven, describing two different heavens. One, a general heaven for everybody; the other, a private heaven filled with everything you loved. I carried the book with me everywhere I went. If I was going to die, I liked this notion of a personal heaven. Another comfort for me.

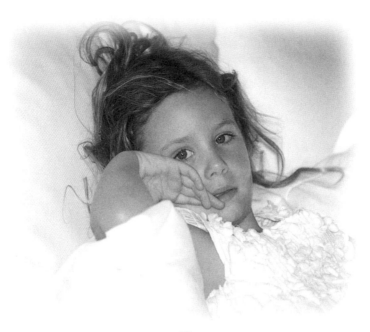

Tess

HEAVEN

To understand my heaven you'd have to know me.
You'd have to know what makes me smile,
what makes a laugh fall out of my face.
There'd be music playing,
definitely dancing,
a great Latin beat.
Magenta bougainvillea would spill out of old
terra-cotta pots.
White houses dotted on hillsides,
Turquoise waters down below,
Sun shining.
Or
Tess and I lying between sheets as soft as clouds,
Arms wrapped around each other in harmony,
Falling asleep with smiles.
Or
Hiking up a hill,
vibrant greens sprinkled with wildflowers.
My husband, my children, my grandchildren,
laughing, talking.
We're all strong, young, powerful – life is easy.
There is nothing to fear.
This is my heaven.

ANOTHER PERFECT DAY

The day would be sunny, not too hot,
a nice breeze with leaves flying around me.
I'd hop into my convertible,
the top down.
I would have a hint of a smile
and anticipation on my lips.
On the radio, Billy Eckstine would be singing,
Everything I have is yours.
I was young, full of hope,
full of life.
My skin would be tan and glistening,
fitting in my clothes like a glove.
I would feel happy,
raring to go.
I'd drive down the highway to the beach,
water shimmering blues and greens,
sand white, hot,
no traffic,
just me,
my convertible,
and my music,
no thoughts in my head.
Anything would be possible.
What a day!
Early this morning I hiked in the dew
with a friend,
laughing and talking as we walked.

I started a painting of an orchid today.
I liked it.
I had Rod Stewart on my CD singing,
It must have been moon-glow.
A lump rose in my throat, bittersweet memories.
Visions of Kim Novak and William Holden
locked in their slow, sexy dance.
My old dog sat at my side on her favorite pillow,
catching a few rays through the window.
Not another sound in the house.
I got into my station wagon, heading for my
favorite place to write.
I turned on the radio —
Steve Tyrell crooning into the microphone.
The sun was shining.
What could be better than that?
I'm grateful,
fifty years later,
for another perfect day.

LOVE

Love is a fire I warm myself by,
fanning it to keep it aglow.
When I'm too tired to fan and
when no one else keeps it up,
the cold and shadows sadden me,
I think I will never feel love again.

I hear my husband fixing our dinner.
He says, *You left some clothes in the closet.*
I open the door and find a bag with a bow,
filled with new clothes.
The love I feel doesn't come from the gift.
It's the picture of him getting in his car,
going to the store, saying, *Yes, I think
this will be perfect for her.*

Or I might get a phone call from my daughter:
Attitude check, are you having a better day today?
That picture overwhelms me with love.
Or the time my son called from Boston,
saying, *I couldn't wait to tell you when I got home,
I had to call you now.*
His peak experience becomes mine.
Oh yes, those fires are crackling.

My friends call: *Can I bring dinner over?*
Can I pick you up? Can I sit with you?
My granddaughter runs past all her friends
in a crowded room, yelling *Nana,*
burying her head in my lap.
My twin grandsons, all bundled up,
blowing me kisses.

These fires are rising, rising.
I'm warmed right down to my bones.

Alexander and Gideon

Left alone, I would have spent those days of waiting frantically making lists, but my friends would not let me. Convinced there was plenty I could do to boost up my immune system, my friend Susan dragged me to an accupuncturist. *She's magic,* she kept insisting. Reluctantly, I went. Indeed, she was magic. I walked into Lonnie's office, and when she took my hand, I started to cry- from relief. Immediately, I knew I was in good hands. I trusted her. In the beginning, I went there three to five times a week. Each visit I cried. By the time my visits pared down to once every three weeks, I stopped crying. I felt stronger. It took a village to keep me going.

I went to a nutritionist named Dale, also a cancer survivor. *Juices,* she said, and juices I drank. My friend Teri went to the market and bought me every fresh vegetable and vitamin imaginable. She bought me a juicer and began blending drinks. While I drank carrot, beet, and celery juice, Bob and Teri drank vodka. They got drunk and cried together.

My friend Julie flew in from Atlanta and stopped at our favorite deli in Los Angeles on her way up to Santa Barbara. We sat at my kitchen table, told stories, and ate. Not the kind of party you want to get invited to. Val stopped by to drop off a gift and Margo brought her homemade chicken soup and answered the constantly ringing phone. It looked like fun, but believe me, it wasn't.

My community of friends and acquaintances amazed me. Letters, food, flowers, and phone calls kept pouring in as news traveled about my condition. Someone was always there to answer it. I couldn't talk. I didn't know what to say. My favorite calls came from friends who said, *You don't have to call me back… we just want to say we're pulling for you.* Sometimes I felt like I was witnessing my own funeral; touching and bizarre at the same time. I'll never forget it.

Surrounded with all this love and support, I watched helplessly as my stomach grew larger from all the probing and procedures. I was tired and scared. The images of my mother and sisters, lying in their beds, their stomachs distended, their bodies wasting away, haunted me.

To me, this meant the end.

WHAT I'D LOVE TO HEAR

Please don't expect me to call you back
Or explain doctor by doctor
Or talk about how I found out
Or where we went
Or what they said
Or exactly how much time they gave me
Or if the kids were there
And how they took it
And how they felt

Tell me instead
You look healthy
Just checking on you
No need to call back
We're praying for you
Hope you are feeling better
We're bringing dinner
What else do you need?
We love you,
We're lighting candles for you
We think of you often
You can do this

No stories about your aunt
Only love me
Only hope for me
Only pray for me
Thank you for caring and
I'll get back to you as soon as I can

THE FINAL DIAGNOSIS

We received the final diagnosis several hellish weeks later. My cancer was the worst imaginable, Leiomyosarcoma (later known as Uteral Stromal Sarcoma) fourth stage, metastasized, inoperable.

I remember hearing the doctor say, *This is what we suggest, Mrs. Fead. First, three weeks of heavy chemo in the hospital – you'll get very sick, you'll lose your hair. When you are healed, we'll resection your stomach. It will be a very slow recovery after which you will need to undergo three more weeks of twenty-four hour a day chemotherapy into the site. Let's see, this is Friday. We should schedule you for Monday. We can't miss this window of opportunity.*

I remember asking, *What if I decide not to do this?* I didn't know if I could survive the treatment, nor did I feel ready to give up my life as I knew it by Monday.

Standing in the hallway of the City of Hope Hospital and in a matter-of-fact tone, these two young doctors said, *Without treatment, we think you have about two months.*

Blur.

White noise.

I didn't hear much else of what they said. I couldn't hear it. For so many years I had been anticipating this moment. My grandmother had cancer at sixty-two. By sixty-three, she was gone. My mother's cancer ran the same course. My two sisters met a similar fate. Thelma, my eldest sister, died at age fifty-five; my middle sister Eileen was sixty-three when she died twelve years ago.

All lost to cancer. At sixty-nine, I was older than any woman in my family has ever lived. I attributed this fact to a few things I'd done to change my life. In my forties, I'd left a difficult marriage, dropped out of the fast lane, and moved to a small town. I ate right and exercised faithfully. In making these changes, I hoped I had taken myself out of harm's way. Even so, I did get cancer twelve years ago; a contained uterine lining cancer that resulted in a hysterectomy. I remember thinking to myself, *Well, that's my cancer – I've beaten it.* But not quite. Apparently, some not-so-contained cells slipped away unnoticed and found their way into my abdomen.

Despite the reputations of these two fine doctors and because they essentially said the same thing – time is of the essence – start immediately – very sick – long recovery – heavy chemo – resection the stomach, we sought the opinion of two more doctors, an oncologist and a surgeon.

Dr. Charles Forscher, from Cedars Sinai in Los Angeles, a very smart and caring oncologist, had done his homework by checking my twelve-year-old slides. He came up with the fact that my cancer cells from my uterine lining had escaped into my abdomen, making my cancer hormone receptive. Our first lifeboat in this sea of terror. My last stop was Dr. Frederick Eilber, a surgical oncologist at UCLA Medical Center. I sat in his office surrounded by my family. He read my tests. Drumming his fingers on the desk, he looked at me and said, *We're not going to operate and we're not going to give you chemo. We're going to give you a pill and a shot. Femara, a drug used for breast cancer, and Lupron, a shot given to prostate cancer patients.* We all started to cry.

But it's in my liver! It's stage four —

His voice was stern when he said, *Wrap your brain around this. We don't care where it is or what stage it's in. If this treatment works, the combination will get to the cancer everywhere. I'll go to the tumor board in the morning to ask for their approval. Meanwhile, go home and keep your chemo appointment just in case. I'll call you after the meeting tomorrow.*

It was a long night. Though trying to be positive, I heard myself say to my husband, *They'll never let him do this.* I didn't believe I could escape chemotherapy and an operation. It would take a miracle for them to approve this experimental treatment. I would have grabbed any alternative, and I believed this doctor.

The next morning the phone rang early. My miracle happened. They approved the treatment! Before hanging up, I made my appointment for my first shot. Then I made another call and cancelled my Monday morning appointment for chemotherapy.

BEGINNINGS

I like to sit on the
sand until I catch
my breath
until everything is
right again.

I like to watch the
waves crash
linger for a moment
and slowly go back
to their beginnings.

Isn't that what we do?
We linger for
only a moment
and then – go slowly back
to our beginnings.

TYPHOON

I'm living a normal life now.
The typhoon is over, the one that lifted me up and
swirled me around
and took off the top of my head.
The typhoon that didn't let me catch my breath or
get my equilibrium,
that wouldn't let me know when or if I would land.
The typhoon that scared me so that I could not
sleep night after night,
that made me weep in the dark.
But I've landed now and I keep watching the
weather reports.
Are the clouds gathering again?
Are they getting darker?
Maybe it was all a dream, like Dorothy's.
Maybe it really never happened.
I'm living a normal life now.
But I'm watching.

GRATEFUL FOR ONE MORE DAY IN THE SUN

I laughed last night,
not a fake laugh with my mouth opening wide
and my eyes downcast with nowhere to go,
but a real laugh from my belly, eyes crinkling,
body shaking.

I danced last night,
not a listless dance but a wild one, music storming
up from my toes to my spine, out my arms, my
heart keeping time to the music.

I cried last night,
not a sad, hard cry, but one of joy,
one of gratitude,
to wake up to turquoise waters,
to languish the days away carelessly,
to be with loved ones.

The month before I learned about my cancer, we bought a house that needed remodeling. After totally gutting the inside, our world turned upside down. Once the initial shock wore off, we wondered if we should sell or continue with the remodel. After hours of debating and interviewing contractors, we decided to remodel but stay within the footprint of the house. There was no time to rebuild our dream house. No time to wait for permits. No big closets. I needed to regain order as soon as possible.

The remodel took nine months. Was it a blessing or a curse? It kept me busy, it made me crazy. This was not an easy time for me. Anyone who has ever remodeled a house knows how frustrating it can be. I had to deal with an absentee contractor and his arrogant son, and two men who designed a bamboo pergola who thought my pockets were lined with gold. There was a cement contractor who one morning answered my husband's pertinent question by saying, *Look, I didn't come here on a Saturday morning to give you an education in cement.*

While recuperating from tests, I'd schlep down to Los Angeles every week to pick out fabrics, oftentimes crying on my drive to the city, wondering if I would live long enough to see my home finished. Each day, fatigue would hit me so hard, that by mid-afternoon I'd have to drag a chair around my house to meet with the workmen. Despite the fact that I'd remodeled homes for myself and other people, I couldn't manage this one. My treatment – the pills and shots – made me loopy. One minute hot, one minute cold, one minute happy, one minute desolate, I never knew what to expect. Each decision was agonizing to make. Finally, I told Bob he had to take over. I just couldn't deal with the workmen anymore.

Deal with them he did. Bob worked and lived in Los Angeles during the week. Every Thursday night he came home and on Fridays he met with the contractors and crew. Thank God he enjoyed the process. It was all too much for me.

Meanwhile, I couldn't sleep at night. No matter how tired I was, my thoughts kept racing. Fabric samples, couch fabrics, paint chips, drapery samples were lying all over our rented house. The chatter was constant inside my head, day and night. I found no island of peace.

The remodeling dragged on month after month. However, I began noticing some changes in the way I felt. I was getting stronger, enough to start working out again. I also decided to see a therapist – to help me plan my death, I thought. But it turned out I needed her to help me learn how to live with cancer.

NO REGRETS

Sacred cows and Indian temples will have to wait for me this time around.

Steamy rivers and great walls will lushly feed the souls of others but probably not mine – this time around.

I won't be packing for a trip to the Congo or taking a boat trip down the Nile this time around either. I know that to be true.

Nor will I be returning to talk with the Masai and taking their faces home with me or sitting once again on a camel's back or feeding a lovely baboon – but I have no regrets.

I have the kind of love that one recognizes across the room – a selfless kind of love of a man that walks to his own drummer and has drummed his way into my heart.

I've lived to laugh with my grandchildren and see their faces smile up at mine, not caring it's no longer perfect.

I've seen and gone to so many places. No, I have no regrets this time around. How could I?

Bob and Bev

BEE HIVE

Neither grand stone houses
surrounded by tall cornfields
nor cloud filled open skies
can quiet my chattering mind.

Neither laughing nights of music and poker
nor bread-filled meals in seaside havens
can quiet my chattering mind.

It matters not how far I travel
or where I choose to go.
My inner life like a hive of bees
buzzes on, and on, and on.

DILEMMA

Why me, God?
Why was I chosen to live when those before me
died so suddenly?
Should I take a stranger's hand to lead her down
a path not known?
Will a child hear a different tune because of what
I sing in her ear?
Are there lessons for me yet to be learned?
I wonder.
What am I to do?
Are there only moments of happiness?
Should I be more productive with my time?
Are moments spent in laughter squandered or
is that indeed exactly what should be done?

TODAY

My laugh has returned.
I can see the joke again.
Petty conversation has crept back into my life.
I'm out into the world away from my safe walls now.
I'm trying not to tell strangers on the street
my plight, my news, my cancer.
I'm making plans for the future again.
I'm eating things that give me pleasure.
I'm no longer scared to go to sleep.
Who knows how this story ends?
Who knows how anybody's story ends?
There is only today.

How do you live with cancer? I had no idea. I only knew I had all these feelings that had no outlet. I was a painter whose work had hung in many galleries, yet I could not pick up a brush even though I knew it might express my feelings.

My poetry class provided that outlet. The facilitator of our group, Perie Longo, was a renowned poet who had lost her husband to cancer. Christine was right, she was kind and gentle. She handed me a pad of paper and pen and though I never dreamed I could write poetry, within minutes words came tumbling out.

The group convened weekly with always four to six people present. From the first meeting, I loved it, the experience reminiscent of my first painting class forty years ago. Each of us so interested to hear what the others had to say, all of us often wrote through our tears. We praised and supported our fellow poets' efforts. I'd leave the group and continue writing at home. Though I hadn't been able to paint since my diagnosis, I was able to describe my feelings with words on paper.

During this time of uncertainty – of wondering if the treatment was working and if so, for how long – I didn't know how to act. Should I prepare to die or go about living as if I had a future? Nightmares plagued my dreams. Because I wasn't sleeping well, I was tired all the time. Our rental house was charming but had lots of steep stairs. My dog had to be carried up and down, and on some days I almost felt liked I needed to be carried, too. The new house was still in chaos and I was always waiting for the other shoe to drop, health wise.

I took pills every day and a shot every three months along with the dreaded CAT (CT) scans. Had my tumors shrunk, stayed the same or had my cancer spread? It was constantly on my mind.

Meanwhile, I continued with my therapy sessions. One day, I asked my therapist if she had any other clients like me, people living with a serious cancer. If there were such people, I needed to meet them. She arranged a meeting. It proved to be one more life-changing event. Eight of us sat in a group sharing our stories. These people stunned me with their bravery, many of them facing not only uncertainty but also debilitating treatments. We all realized that if we lived in another time and place, we would not have survived this long. Our gratitude was almost tangible. With our therapist leading the way, we decided to do an art project together. We called it "The Aphrodite Project." Each of us created an art piece that depicted the journey our cancer had led us on.

I opted to paint a self-portrait with a poem titled "Tears" scrolled down one side of it. This was my first attempt at painting in several months and I was nervous. At our first meeting Justin and Jenny, two talented volunteers, filmed us, as our therapist Jo-Anne led us in conversation. My painting flowed out of me much as my poetry had. It felt so good to have a brush in my hand again. The music played and my dog sat on her cushion, just like in the old days. The smell of paint and turpentine filled the room with its fragrance. I felt happy and whole. I felt like the old me. After completing my self-portrait, I began to paint again.

The two volunteers that filmed us became producer and editor and turned "The Aphrodite Project" into a documentary. It is being shown all over the country to oncologists and at film festivals. Our hope is that people living with cancer will be helped by it.

One day recently, I had a sumptuous lunch with my new friend Sue, also a stage four cancer survivor. She turned to me and said, *If this is stage four, there must be a stage five and six!*

That's cancer today.

TEARS

My tears are not always out of sadness, you know, nor
do they come from only loneliness, or fear, or distress.
There are joyful tears and tears of blinding love.
My eyes fill up when others reach for their dream and
achieve it,
when a young couple unashamedly show love
for their children,
when a mother's hand lingers in her boy's hair.
How long ago was it I had my hand in my boy's hair?
There are bittersweet tears.
When looking at a hauntingly beautiful sunset I'm
reminded that my sunsets are no longer limitless.
Knowing that great passion and heightened
moments of beginning love cannot last forever brings
tears to my eyes, even knowing that something
wonderful replaces them.
Looking at a young girl in a pale sleeveless dress
stings my eyes with tears.
How long ago was I in that dress?
Would I rather see the sunset and feel the passion and
endure the tears?
Oh yes.

My tears are not always out of sadness, you know, nor do they come only out of loneliness or of fear or distress. There are happiness tears, tears of amazement or blinding love. My eyes fill up when others reach for their dream and achieve it, when a young couple unashamedly show love for their children with the Mothers hand lingering in her boys hair. How long ago was it I had my hands in my childs hair. There are bittersweet tears, when looking at a hauntingly beautiful sunset I will be reminded that my sunsets are no longer limitless. Knowing that great passion and heightend moments of beginning love cannot last forever, brings tears to my eyes even knowing that something wonderful replaces it. Looking at youth in a pale sleeveless dress stings my eyes with tears. How long ago was it I was in that dress? Would I rather see the sunset, feel the passion and endure the tears?

Oh Yes

VULNERABLE

What is it you're frightened of? asks my warrior side.
What fills your heart with such dread?
*What happened to the coat of bravery you wore so
confidently?*
I feel like a deer sometimes, I answer.
I'm not always like you.
I want to lie down in flower-kissed pastures,
Let my eyes close against the sun.
I don't want to be poised for battle, I say,
My buttons can't always cover what's inside,
Don't be disappointed with what you see, I plead.
More kindly now, my warrior side asks
But what is it you are really frightened of?
The possibilities of the inevitable,
I manage to say in my soft deer voice.

THE LUXURY OF DENIAL

Every morning when I wake, I have to face
my older-than-I-want-to-look face,
my softer-than-I-want-to-have body,
my endless list of must-do meaningless errands
and just when I think that is enough reality
for the day
my eyes light on my keep-me-alive pills
a reminder of where I am in this time-capsule life
I long for the luxury of denial.
Perhaps putting gauze on the mirrors would help,
pretending my pills are vitamins preparing me for
a long run
Strong legs at the starter blocks,
no knees that hurt,
no thumbs that ache
no CAT scans,
no doctors to see,
no thinking at night,
only peaceful sleep,
as though I were young once again.

It's Between You and God Now

Eleven months after my diagnosis and after undergoing a CAT scan, I had the opportunity to speak to Dr. Fred Kass, my oncologist at Santa Barbara Cancer Center, alone, without my husband and children present. Just the two of us talking; no medical terms this time. Just frank stuff.

Well, doctor, I asked, *what do you think? What kind of time are we talking about? How long can this go on?*

My doctor said, *We never dreamed you would do so well, Beverlye. As far as expectations go, you are off the charts. I think it's between you and God now.*

Goose bumps appeared on my arms. Though his words were sobering, I appreciated his honesty. Then he said, *You know, in a way, you're lucky because you've had a warning that most people don't get.*

We both had tears in our eyes as we continued talking. As I left his office he said, *Come in for a CAT scan whenever you want. If you get scared, come in earlier than three months. If you feel great, don't come in for four months. You may not be in control of your illness, but you can definitely be in control of this.* He smiled. *And if you ever need to talk in between CAT scans, just call me.*

I left his office feeling a bit like Blanche Du Bois might have felt – depending on the kindness of strangers. My doctor is right, I am lucky. The tumors have remained the same. I'm living with cancer, it's the newest thing. You don't cure it, you live with it.

Later on as I reflected on his words, this thought came to me: maybe it's between each of us and God. It's impossible for any of us to guess what tomorrow holds, so look around and enjoy each blessing. What else can we possibly ask for?

Only time.

ALL THE TIME I NEED

It's funny but now that time is running out,
I have all the time I need to be myself.
My days and nights have more hours now.
I allow myself naps in the sun,
and daydreams on the couch.
I stare out the window to watch a hummingbird
light on a perfect leaf, and marvel at the beauty.
I no longer have to do anything
and because of that I have time to do everything.
More watching, listening.
More painting, writing.
Luckily for me, time is standing still.

THE UNINVITED GUEST

I feel fortunate my tumors came to me
in the fall of my life,
for at this stage,
I'm grateful for this uninvited wake-up call.
My days are more meaningful to me now.
Would I have taken the time to appreciate
all my blessings in the summer of my life?
No, I think not.
Would I have noticed how healing the sun feels
on my face and arms
and let it rest there so carelessly?
Would I have appreciated the beautiful images
the moon makes in the still of the night?
No, I have my tumors to thank for that.
And so I do.
Thank you.

BOOK IT!

After leaving the doctor's office, I called Bob and asked, *Remember we said we weren't going back to Europe this year because of our remodeling expenses?* He said, *Go on,* and so I told him what my doctor said about me and God. When I added how well I was feeling, Bob answered with just two words: *Book it.*

We put the wheels in motion to return to Capri, our favorite vacation spot on earth, our home away from home. We caught an Air France plane to Paris and stayed three days. We spent another three days in Brittany with good friends before traveling on to our beloved Capri.

In Paris, I sat in a little café on the Rives Gauche musing over the events of the past year. I never thought I'd see this magical city again but there I was, strolling along the boulevards as though I had nothing in my stomach but divine French food.

From Paris, we drove to Brittany and spent three days with friends feasting some more. After saying our good-byes, we set off for our favorite place on earth, The Isle of Capri.

More friends waited for us there. We arrived and I felt totally relaxed as usual. But this trip, I also felt gratitude I hadn't felt before. Bittersweet maybe. My dear Capri, its healing blue waters and white houses dotting the lush hillsides, thank you for welcoming us back once more!

We spent a blissful week eating and drinking, fresh pastas, tasty salads, lots of red wine, and always dessert. Bob savored the rich Terre di Tufi wine. I couldn't get enough of the fresh arugula. We acted like we didn't have a care in the world.

Only when we left did I feel sadness as I looked at our beloved Capri. Would this be my last visit? Would this be my last look? I somehow didn't think so.

Mother and Dad

LOVE LETTERS
DISCOVERED

My nephew sent me some letters last month,
letters from my parents from a long-ago
trip to Europe.
Embarrassed by her handwriting,
my mother never wrote to us.
My father did all the correspondence
with his elegant loopy letters.
Two things surprised me in these letters:
One was that he wrote so lovingly,
I had forgotten that side of him.
I remembered him only at the end.
He was bitter then, though still handsome
in that older, Clark Gable way.
He was always sharply dressed,
black and silver hair slicked back,
and he had those devastating eyes,
only slightly diminished by age.
It was difficult to see him in the last few years.
His glamorous lifestyle and flamboyance
had been replaced by a dreary way of life.
Only a few remembrances of his glory days
were there in his sunless apartment.
It made him angry.
It made me sad.
How differently he sounded in those letters
from long ago.

One exclaimed how beautiful my mother looked,
what a wonderful trip they were having.
I could picture them dining and dancing on the
ship, she all dressed up in her blue beaded gown
and he all dandified in his custom-made tuxedo.
They were such a beautiful couple.
Here came the second surprise:
In another one of his letters, he said they had found
the most glorious place in all the world.
We only hope you girls can go there one day, he wrote.
It's called the Isle of Capri.
Strangely enough, we think it's the most beautiful
place in the world too, Daddy. It's our favorite place
to go also.
Now I understand why I feel so at home there.
Maybe you and mother left a little bit of yourselves
to welcome us to Capri.
That's the piece of the puzzle I hadn't put in yet.
With all the places in the world, and with never
knowing you'd been there, we come back to Capri
year after year.
And just maybe it's to catch a glimpse of the two
of you smoking your Pall Malls and drinking your
coffee under the chiming clock tower in the piazza.

EVERYONE NAPS IN CAPRI

Everyone naps after lunch in Capri
Lined up facing the sea
The older ladies
In their black house dresses
Walking from market
To home
Plump hands clutching
Their heavy bags
Slump down on a bench
In front of their casas
Eyes closed
Faces turned toward the sea
The rich in their elegant La Perla
Bathing suits
Their bodies bent into sleeping shapes
Like twigs fallen
From a tree
They lie on rocks
At the beach
Chairs at the pool
Faces slack with contentment
Bellies filled with wine
Bodies warmed by sun
Everyone naps in Capri
All lined up facing the sea

EYES, STOMACH, HEART AND SOUL

I received two gifts this month,
gifts I never thought I'd have again.
One for the eyes and stomach —
Paris.
It filled our eyes with beauty,
marching down the Champs Elysee
like two soldiers
holding hands
looking to the right and
to the left
smelling fresh breads
and hearing the sounds of the city
our stomachs bulging with pommes frites and foie-gras.
Ah, but returning to Capri was the gift that fed our
hearts and soul.
Velvet waters
silk skies
rocks like mountains
clouds lined up like the New York skyline
and always that healing sun
like nowhere else on earth.

LETTING GO

Writing makes me think about my parents and my sisters, all of them gone. My memories are sweet and sad. I wonder how many families escape doing unforgivable things to each other? I wonder how we learn to forgive? Often, my sisters visit me in my dreams. I think about them when we were all young. And sometimes when I'm driving, I carry on conversations with them as if they are sitting in my car, listening to me talk.

I think about my children when they were young, during that wonderful time of our lives – the innocence on their little faces etched in my mind forever. I hope they live long enough to forgive me for whatever ways I have hurt them. I am so proud of them as adults and as the parents they've become.

I think about my grandchildren. How lucky I am to have them enter my heart, their sweetness so delicious to me. Their love more healing than any pill I could ever take. How I'd love to see who and what they will grow up to become. The ego in me hopes they carry something of me to help them whenever they need it in life.

Facing my mortality makes me realize how much of what my parents and sisters worked for – all that they held dear – really didn't matter after all. The same can be said for me. Everything that seemed so important, had to be done a certain way, doesn't matter any more, and so each day I try to let go just a little bit more. That's what I hope, at the end of the day – to learn how to let go.

TRAIN RIDES

Roast beef reminds me of train rides with my sister.
Kindly porters in black caps and white teeth.

This way little ladies, they'd say
while we waited for a table in the dining car.
We'd watch the trees run by our window.
We'd order roast beef with horseradish,
mashed potatoes, and milk.

Later, my sister would button my pajamas.
Put me to sleep next to her on our berth,
behind the blue curtain,
our few belongings at our feet in the net pocket.

Was she old enough to take care of me then?
She was ten, I was five.
Once we went to visit cousins;
another time – our eldest sister, husband and baby.

Were we always sent away on trains holding hands?
asked my dying sister many years later.

What was our mother doing that was so important?

ABSOLUTION

I saw an old photo of my eldest sister the other day.
Long, luxurious brown hair to her shoulders.
Her handsome husband sitting contentedly beside her.
It was inconceivable to picture her years later,
in the hospital bed, bald head, eyes too bright.
Are you happy you stayed married, Thelma?
Oh yes, she said. *I could never picture my life*
without him.
I was happy for her, but
That wasn't the answer I was looking for.
I wanted her forgiveness if I left my marriage.
I needed absolution.
I wanted to know what to do with my life.

Thelma and Victor Selten

Terry, Beverlye and Jim

PHOTOS: A CONVERSATION WITH MY KIDS

I didn't know what it meant
to break a family apart
and with it, everyone's heart.
Forgive me,
for I did not know.
The memories crushed of
skiing, tennis, and sailing
together,
always together.
Afternoons of baseball games and
dance recitals,
photos of four smiling faces.
How could I have known
my actions would leave a gap that could never
be filled?
I was a young girl.
He was a young boy.
He knew my family.
I knew his.
The world was ours.
What went wrong?
To save one life, do you throw away three?
How could we have guessed
the photos would someday be ripped apart?
Forgive me
for I did not know.

MY LIFE

My life is my life now,
even though it wasn't always so.
I fought a long,
hard battle
for this privilege.
There were many casualties
along the way.
There were so many achingly
unsure moments,
I wanted to move forward,
I wasn't sure I could.
Old voices hung in my ear
to hinder me,
I stumbled,
moving on to what,
I wondered.
Then a point of no return,
finally
crossover to freedom.

DREAMS

I dream my dreams early in the morning when
the sheets cocoon around me.
The temperature is perfect in the room and the pillow
creates a movie screen for the images I'm seeing.
My sisters come to visit, one by one,
sometimes together.
I thought you were dead, I say.
No we're not, they answer.
Has it all been a joke?
Can we all be together again?
My parents visit too.
Does my mother forgive me for not always
understanding her?
Will my father tell me things I need to hear?
Don't go yet, I say. *Please stay. I love
having you all here.*
My dreams stay with me all day. I wait for the night.
One sister comes in the morning light.
I'm happy to see her.
Can I come with you? I ask.
Not yet, she coos. *But I've missed you so much.*
It's only a dream, she says, and is gone.
Was it only a dream?
Will they lead the way when it's time?

Twelve years after my middle sister Eileen died from cancer, I sat in the same Fisher Living Room that I had built, and waiting for my own cancer treatment.

Three months into treatment, I had my first CAT scan. My husband, my kids and friends Bobbie and Eddie accompanied me. While waiting for the scan to be read, we went to breakfast. There was a lot of laughter covering up the tension.

Thirty minutes later, my internist, Dr. Kurt Ransohoff called my cell phone. *Beverlye, we need the radiologist to really read this, but to me it looks like the tumors have shrunk, some maybe by twenty-five percent.*

With my thumb up, I reported the news to my support team. We all cheered in the restaurant. A monumental moment! Since then, every three months I monitor the progress of my tumors by undergoing a CAT scan. Initially, my family and close friends put reminder notes on their calendars. Each time I had a scan, my husband called my daughter who called my son and one friend who called others until everyone knew.

Today, my husband and I go alone. Most people don't even realize I'm still having CAT scans. The tumors have remained the same size. As hard as this is to believe, sometimes I forget that I have cancer. I'm in relatively no pain except for an occasional twinge in my abdomen. Last month, I was so busy living my life,

I forgot to get my Lupron shot. The doctor's office had to call to remind me. Cancer no longer consumes my whole life. We're back to every day living.

As it should be.

Eric, Terry, Bob, Beverlye, Jim, Leslie

WHAT DOES IT ALL MEAN?

My daughter says *we'll love it out of you.*
My son says *I think we've bought some time.*
My husband says *you're not going anywhere.*
My doctors say *it's stabilized.*
My friends say *you're so lucky.*
My family says *it's a miracle.*
And I say *what the hell does all that mean?*
And I say *there's a sleeping giant inside of me,*
and how do I keep him quiet?
And I say *I'm still scared.*
And I say *it is a miracle. I am lucky.*
Today I am alive and living life.

CAT SCAN

tense
afraid
frail
tired
alone
cold

drink the drink,
pure chalk, once, twice, three times
lie down –
in —— out
breath longer
in ——————— out

it's over
I'm cold as the floor
get dressed quickly
shakily waiting
for the call

about
my
life

NOT DONE YET

One day across a lunch table
after hearing the news about my health,
a dear friend asked me,
Are you done yet, Beverlye?
No, I said.
I'm not done yet.
And then he thought for a moment
and said,
Okay then,
you're not done.
And that's that.

SELF

I want others to think of me
as strong as stone
but soft like a bird in a hand.
I want to be thought of with a paintbrush,
painting the world a myriad of beautiful colors.
I want to be pictured as a rocket
full of energy and fire,
but quiet enough to sit
in my garden and listen to my thoughts.
I want to be seen as growing
like Alice in Wonderland,
expanding in all directions year after year.
And finally,
I want to be pictured on a sandy beach
being healed by all the beauty and love
surrounding me.

Beverlye at eighteen

A LETTER TO AN OLD PAL

You wouldn't know me anymore
You'd probably laugh at me now
I listen to NPR
Rarely drink
Watch mortgage rates and CNN
Poetry and paintings are my pastimes now
I prefer early to bed
I rarely go to parties
I never go dancing and
Flirting bores me
Some nights I really enjoy eating alone
Well, what's left of you? You ask
I still love to laugh, I say
I adore small children
And smaller dogs
Music, sun, and water are still my favorites
And every once in a while
When the moon is full
And the night is right
I sing and dance my heart out
Just like in the old days

BEV'S TEAM

Very shortly after my diagnosis and still during the very crazy time, friends of ours, Judy and Peter, organized a cancer walk within a cancer walk. The event was for the Santa Barbara Cancer Center, but our friends rounded up over fifty people and ordered tee shirts with *Bev's Team* written on them. They got everyone there on a Sunday morning at 8:30 AM to walk 3.2 miles (even me and Bob). As far as your eyes could see, was Bev's Team – it was quite a thrill. A wonderful feeling of love and support again from the community, combined with one of my favorite things to do – raising money for cancer.

We had Bev's Team this year, too, and my friend Peter said, *Next year we have to find someone else to have this for, because obviously you're not sick anymore.*

From his mouth into God's ear, as they say.

YOUTH ON PARADE

I think about youth a lot lately.
The sheer beauty of it.
The vulnerability of it.
I can't stop watching and admiring it.
Skin like clean canvas
Arms, legs like colts,
long and nimble.
Innocence as if nothing could happen.
It exaggerates my years, my weathered wisdom.
I become ancient in their wake.
Now I understand the multitudes of old people
sitting on benches, watching the parade
of beauty and vitality go by,
sucking it up for themselves.
If only it were that easy.

FRESH FACES

Everyone had fresh faces, skinned knees,
dewy innocence
one time or another,
We weren't born with tired eyes that have seen
too much,
brown spots showing up on hands as though
kissed by moths,
or bones that are knit together by sunlight.
We were all gladiators once with shiny hair
and nimble limbs.
We never meant to become the old folks,
listened to,
reckoned with,
frightened of.
Those fresh faces are still inside us.
We're still here, they say to passersby.
Look at us, we're still here.

MAKE PLANS AND GOD LAUGHS

And so life marches on as if it didn't know I had cancer at all. It throws me all the regular curves everyone else is pitched; visits to the dentist, a bout of shingles, friends passing away, and a huge loss for us, the passing of our beloved dog, Bacall. I'm reminded each time I walk into my home and only silence greets me how much I miss her wagging her tail, barking her welcome and licking me with kisses.

Accepting loss is such a huge lesson to learn. Being the last one standing is not always the easiest position. Here I am, the last one remaining of a family all taken by cancer, and I'm still standing. Twenty-four months after being diagnosed with the worst possible version of this disease, I picture my doctors standing beside me, all of us shaking our heads pleased and confounded by the wonderful outcome.

This last July I turned seventy years old. There was a time when seventy sounded so old to me. But time changes your perspective. Now when I hear that someone is turning seventy-five, I think to myself-that person still has plenty of good years left.

I REMEMBER

I remember when I thought thirty was old
then I thought fifty was a fresh start and now
I think, here I am at seventy, a baby tadpole
dipping a toe in fresh waters
taking new chances, new risks
seeing life through wise eyes
with a touch of abandon
I like this feeling of irreverence
It thrills me
this not caring
What if I fail?
No matter
the only failing is
not dipping the toe in
The rest is a gold medal

YOU CAN QUOTE ME

You've got to have some fun.
Otherwise, what's life all about?
Going to school?
Getting a job?
Getting married?
Getting your retirement?
Getting a diagnosis?
No, you've got to have some fun.
Otherwise you've just been
marking time.
And you can quote me!

A Year of Hope

As of this writing, it's been twenty-four months since I began my experimental treatment – one shot every three months and one pill every day. Other than the residual shock that lingers from the first news regarding my diagnosis, I am my old self again, but with a difference. I play golf, exercise daily, have fun with my family and savor every sweet moment with them. However, the new me has a passionate need to reach out to cancer patients and pass along what I have learned.

I believe we are all generals of our own lives, sick or well. It's up to us what course we take. Get the best advice you can find, talk it over with your loved ones and then trust your gut feelings. There are no guarantees but at least with this course of action, you remain in charge of your life.

If I could personally talk to you, I would say this: let your loved ones know how much you love them every day. Do something creative, it helps you feel immortal. Exercise as much as you can, it keeps you strong mentally and physically. Write down your thoughts, they will live forever. We are not going to be forgotten.

None of us have control over how or when we exit this life, but we do have some control over our everyday living. Let only those you love walk through your front door. Do what makes you happy. Throw away your clutter. Give as much as you can to causes and people you believe in. It's not what we're dealt, but how we handle what's dealt to us that counts.

And above all – laugh.

Beverlye at three

I CAN DO THIS

I found a posture
early on
hands on hips
head to the side
an attitude
to bolster myself

I'm not alone, it said
I feel my strength
no matter what
life brings
I can do this

UPDATE

July 2008

I feel so blessed to have been given these extra years to help fight cancer.

In 2005, I was honored as a Woman Of Action for the Israel Cancer Research Fund. In 2006 I became Legislative Ambassador for the American Cancer Society and have signed on for two more years. I've been lucky to spend time in both Washington D.C. and Sacramento, CA working towards getting bills passed for cancer research. I serve on the regional council of the American Cancer Society, both the auxiliary board for the Cancer Center as well as the Breast Resource Center both of Santa Barbara. Giving hope and inspiration is my goal when speaking to different groups and gatherings.

My second book "Nana What's Cancer?" is being published by the American Cancer Society and will be in stores by the end of the year. It was co-written with my ten-year-old granddaughter, Tess and explains cancer to children in a non-scary format.

It is now six years later, and while all of my tumors are still there, they are 99% stable. I feel great and can do everything I want! My passion remains my family, and helping to find a cure for cancer. Next week, I will celebrate my 74th birthday.

I am honored to be connected with Stand Up To Cancer, and believe in their profound message, "This is where the end of cancer begins". A portion of this book's proceeds will go to their wonderful cause.

website: http://beverlyehymanfead.com

A c k n o w l e d g e m e n t s

MY ANGELS

Thank you to my dear friend and internist, Dr. Kurt Ransohoff, who originally found the mass in my abdomen, and to Dr. Fred Kass, who has helped me through this. Thank you to Carole Sukman, Dick and Annette Bloch, and Dr. Ernie Rosenbaum for their sound advice. Thank you to Dr. Fredrick Eilber and Dr. Charles Forscher, who came up with the experimental treatment Femara and Lupron.

Thank you to my dear angels, Bobbi and Eddie, Julie and Jamie, Teri and Kenny, Margo and Jeff, Val and Bob, Trish, Sharol, and Wayne, Tony and Carin and Susan and Robert. They all drove me, cooked for me, walked with me and took care of me.

Thank you to Peter and Judy for Bev's Team. Thank you to Lynn for all her help, and to Faye, Gil, Lois, Bobby E., Leslye and Eddie, Morry and Irma for all their support. Thank you to all my amazing friends who wrote me letters, sent me flowers, and called.

Thank you to Jeremy, Ashleigh, Kelsey and Kori for their enthusiasm, and to Bo Criss Design.

Thank you to Lonnie Wu, Lorena Gutierrez, Jo-Anne Blatter, Dr. Jim Adams, and Dale Figtree, who helped heal me with such heart. Thank you to Melody and Judy, who encouraged me into the world of writing. Thank you to Christine Picket who led me to poetry. Thank you to my dear poetry mentor, Perie Longo, and to Lois Klein, who helped me so thoughtfully. Thanks to Montecito Journal's Jim Buckley and to the Santa Barbara Cancer Center's Rick Scott. Thank you to Marla Miller of the Santa Barbara Writers' Conference for her fine editorial input and to Tatiana and Vickie who showed me the light at the end of the tunnel. Thank you to the Kreiss and Selten families for all their love and support. And thank you to my father for his love of his Fisher girls.

Thank you to Micheal, Tera, Jackson, Laurel, and Max for your caring and support. And last but not least, my heartfelt thanks to my wonderfully supportive husband Bob and my dear children Terry, Eric, Leslie, and Jim, and their children Tessa, Gideon and Alexander who have been with me every step of the way and have given me such joy.

Birthday Celebration

TOGETHER

I won't kid you
There are people who do die
from cancer
But more than ever now
There are people who do not
Let you and I, together,
be the ones
who do not

About the Author

Beverlye Hyman Fead is a California artist and writer. Beverlye was raised and educated in Los Angeles. She studied art at UCLA, then continued her studies privately. In 1984, she moved to Santa Barbara. She's had one-person shows in Los Angeles, Aspen, and New York, along with several group shows. During this period, she also wrote travel and sports articles for magazines. For a period of ten years, Hyman Fead designed ceramics, going to Deruta, Italy, and working in the factory of Ubaldo Grazia. Restaurants in Santa Barbara that carry her ceramics include Stella Mare, Mollies, and Cava.

Her love of flowers and fruit is evident in every painting she does. Recently, orchids and her Zen environment have inspired her new series.

Diagnosed with cancer in late 2002, Beverlye combined poetry with her old love, painting. Her first subject matter was a self-portrait with her poem "Tears" painted on it. Beverlye's piece was then digitalized for a cancer project. Her collection of poetry written during this time has become the basis for this book.

Having lost her grandmother, mother, and both sisters to cancer, Beverlye has devoted a great deal of time to cancer on many levels. One of them was raising money and helping to create a waiting room, called the Fisher Living Room, for cancer patients in Santa

Barbara Cancer Center. The room is filled with her paintings and ceramics.

Beverlye also walked sixty-four miles from Santa Barbara to Malibu, California in the Avon three-day walk for breast cancer, while raising money for the cause in 1999. In 2004 she co-chaired with two other women and a committee of eight to raise $500,000 for the first digital mammography machine for Santa Barbara at the Sansum Clinic.

Her hope is to be able to continue raising money for cancer through her writing, painting, and activism. Writing and painting are now Beverlye's "healing treatment" of choice.